CW00409056

ISABELLA & BLODWEN

CAST
IRON
BOOKS

This edition first published in 2023

Cast Iron Books, 17 Clarence Street, Ulverston, Cumbria, LA12 7JJ

www.castironbooks.com

© Rachael Smith

Written & Illustrated by: Rachael Smith

A CIP record for this book is available from the British Library

ISBN: 978-1-8382241-8-9 (hardback)
ISBN: 978-1-8382241-9-6 (ebook)

Printed and bound in the UK

1 2 3 4 5 6 7 8 9

ISABELLA & BLODWEN

RACHAEL SMITH

Dedication

For the real Suzanne MacLeod.

SIGH IF YOU *MUST* KNOW, THE MUSEUM TRIP WAS A LAST-MINUTE ADDITION TO THIS WEEK'S ACTIVITIES. I HAD ALREADY ALLOTTED THE TIME IN MY REVISION SCHEDULE.

NOW I SHALL HAVE TO RE-ARRANGE. I DISLIKE RE-ARRANGING.

I RUN A *VERY* TIGHT SHIP WITH MY REVISION SCHEDULES.

I DON'T DOUBT IT.

I'M NOT LIKE *OTHER GIRLS*, SHAUN. FOR A START I'M NOT A COMPLETE *IDIOT*.

HAHA! I KNOW.

LISTEN, ISABELLA... MY MUM WAS SAYING THAT-

SHAUN.

WHILST I APPRECIATE YOUR ENTHUSIASM, I'D REALLY RATHER WALK TO MY BUS STOP IN *SILENCE*. ALRIGHT?

OH, UH...

SO, IF YOU WOULDN'T MIND WAITING HERE FOR A MOMENT, IT'LL GIVE ME A HEAD START AND WE CAN AVOID ANY AWKWARDNESS.

THAT WOULD BE BEST, DON'T YOU THINK?

OH, RIGHT YOU ARE...

I GUESS I'LL JUST, I... I CAN JUST WATCH THE BOATS FOR A BIT THEN.

WHATEVER FLOATS *YOURS*.

OH THANK GOD! WE WERE WORRIED ABOUT YOU, ISABELLA!

OOOOPS! HAHAHA!

YES...YOU ALL SEEM POSITIVELY *RELIEVED*...

SORRY TO HAVE CAUSED SUCH *DISTRESS*...

HAHAHA! HAHAHA HA!

CLICK

HOW WAS YOUR DAY, HUN? ARE YOU WORKIN' WITH PROFESSOR PIERCE AGAIN TONIGHT?

HE HE HEE! HA HA HA HA! HAA!

MY DAY WAS TEDIOUS. AND NO, I'M-

DO YOU TWO REALLY HAVE NOTHING BETTER TO DO THAN IMBIBE CHEAP WINE AND LAUGH AT YOUR OWN HANDS?!

"IMBIBE!!"

OH MY *GAAWD*!! SHE'S TOO MUCH! AHAHAHAHA!

NO, ACTUALLY.

SIT

I WAS *GONNA* SAY, I'M HERE IF YOU NEED SOMEONE TO TALK TO, OR IF YOU NEED ANY HELP WITH ANYTHING ...Y'KNOW, IF YOU'RE FEELING OVERWHELMED.

I THINK IT'S BRILLIANT THAT YOU'RE WORKIN' SO HARD AND THAT YOU'RE SO AMBITIOUS. IT'S *REALLY* ADMIRABLE, ISSY!

BUT...IT'S ALSO OK TO HAVE A BIT OF FUN WHILE YOU'RE HERE TOO. LIBBY AND AMANDA ARE JUST SHARING A BOTTLE OF WINE AFTER A HARD DAY, MAYBE DON'T JUDGE THEM SO HARSHLY.

AFTER ALL, WE ALL NEED A BIT OF *FUN* AND A BIT OF COMPANY SOMETIMES, RIGHT? OTHERWISE IT WOULD BE QUITE A DULL LIFE, HAHA!

RIGHT, ISSY?

IF YOU'RE DONE THEN PLEASE CAN YOU LEAVE? I'D LIKE TO READ IN *PEACE*.

"CLICK"

BEEP
BEEP
BEEP

SMAK

05:59

06:00

06:00

06:00

06:00

ISABELLA'S MORNING ROUTINE

SHOWER: EXACTLY TEN MINUTES...

TEETH CLEANING:
EXACTLY THREE MINUTES...

DRESSING: EXACTLY FOUR MINUTES...

HAIR: EXACTLY TWO MINUTES...

MAKE BREAKFAST:
EXACTLY SIX MINUTES...

EAT BREAKFAST:
EXACTLY FIVE MINUTES...

SOME LIGHT READING:
ONE HOUR FORTY MINUTES...

...AAAND WE'RE DONE!

BIT EARLY FOR A SATURDAY ISN'T IT? I'VE NOT EVEN HAD BREAKFAST!

UM. WHY ARE YOU EVEN *HERE?* I THOUGHT YOU DID GARDEN CENTRE STUDIES OR SOMETHING.

PLANT SCIENCE!

YEAH, I DON'T THINK IT'S REALLY GOING TO LINK IN WITH MY DEGREE MUCH, BUT PITT RIVERS IS ONE OF MY MUM'S *FAVOURITE* PLACES, SHE'S REALLY–

RIGHT, OK. I'M SURE YOUR MOTHER IS DELIGHTFUL BUT I'D REALLY RATHER PREPARE FOR THE MUSEUM TRIP–

–*IN SILENCE.* GOTCHA. DON'T WORRY, I DON'T MIND.

I DON'T THINK THE SECURITY IS ALL *THAT* TIGHT THOUGH...

YEAH I KNOW, BUT WE'LL STILL HAVE TO BE QUICK!

WE DON'T EVEN KNOW *WHAT* WE'RE GONNA STEAL YET...

I SAY SOMETHING REALLY SMALL.

NOT TOO SMALL THOUGH! IT'S GOT TO BE PRETTY *IMPRESSIVE!*

NO, LISTEN I'VE BEEN LOOKING AT THE WEBSITE, I'VE GOT SOME IDEAS.

CAN WE HELP YOU??

GOSH, WHO WOULD EVER STEAL FROM A *MUSEUM?* THEY CAN'T BE SERIOUS. DO YOU THINK THEY'RE JOKING?

SIGH.

UM...ISABELLA? WE'RE HERE NOW. WE CAN GET OFF.

JUST A SECOND.

OK.

THAT WAS NICE OF YOU...TO LET THEM ALL GO FIRST LIKE THAT.

MM-HM.

OUR MUSEUM DISPLAYS ARCHAEOLOGICAL AND ETHNOGRAPHIC OBJECTS FROM ALL PARTS OF THE WORLD AND ALL TIME PERIODS.

IT WAS FOUNDED IN 1884 WHEN GENERAL PITT RIVERS GAVE HIS COLLECTION TO THE UNIVERSITY OF OXFORD.

THERE WERE MORE THAN 26,000 OBJECTS IN 1884, BUT NOW THERE ARE MORE THAN HALF A MILLION IN THE MUSEUM.

THE MUSEUM HAS ALWAYS BEEN HOUSED IN THIS SMALL THREE GALLERIED BUILDING AT THE REAR OF THE MUSEUM OF NATURAL HISTORY.

EUROPE, ENGLAND, SUSSEX HOVE

IN MOST ETHNOGRAPHIC AND ARCHAEOLOGICAL MUSEUMS THE OBJECTS ARE ARRANGED ACCORDING TO GEOGRAPHICAL OR CULTURAL AREAS...

HERE THEY ARE ARRANGED ACCORDING TO *TYPE*. MUSICAL INSTRUMENTS, WEAPONS, MASKS, TEXTILES, JEWELLERY, ETC.

SCARPER

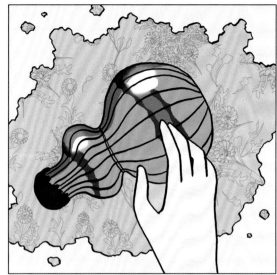

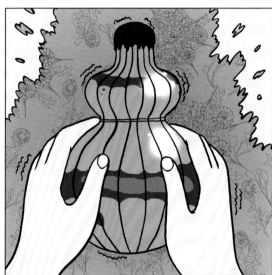

Silvered and stoppered bottle said to contain a witch. Obtained about 1915 from an old lady living in a village near HOVE, SUSSEX. She remarked "and they do say there be a witch in it, and if you let un out there'll be a peck o' trouble."

WHAT ON *EARTH* WAS I THINKING?! IF ANYONE FINDS OUT ABOUT THIS I CAN KISS MY PLACE AT THIS UNIVERSITY GOODBYE...

LET ALONE THE SUMMER INTERNSHIP... MY CAREER WOULD BE OVER BEFORE IT'S EVEN *BEGUN!*

SLAM!

Hello oooo!!

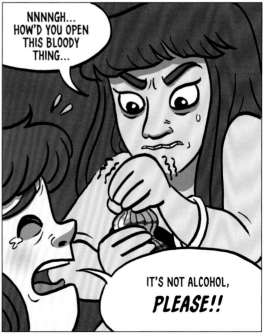

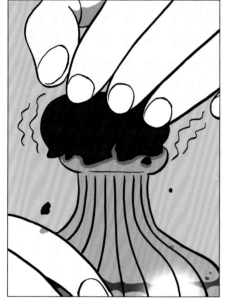

...

ISABELLA...?

ISABELLA, I'M SO SORRY ABOUT WHAT JUST HAPPENED...

...CAN I COME IN, HUN...?

SH...

SHIT OFF!!!

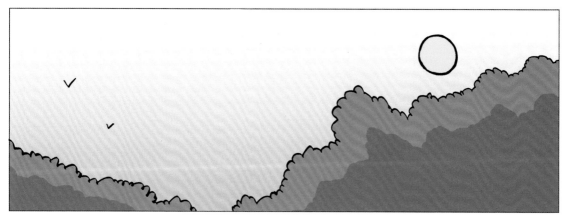

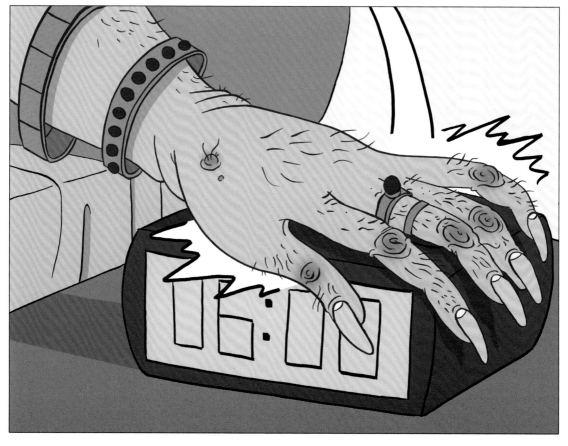

SCRAMBLE →

WHO—

KNOCK KNOCK

KNOCK
KNOCK
KNOCK
KNOCK
"KNOCK"

shhhh!

ISABELLA?!
ISSY, ARE YOU OK?
WE HEARD
SCREAMING!

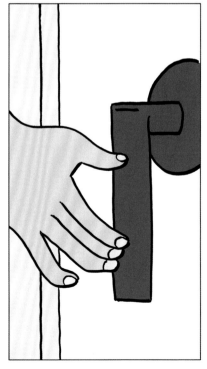

OH YES! I AGREE! I'M REALLY EXCITED ABOUT THIS LECTURE! PROFESSOR PIERCE'S PERCEPTIVE AND DELICATE ANALYSIS OF FOLKLORE IS ABSOLUTELY *FASCINATING!*

ER, SURE. HIS BUM'S NICE TOO, EH?

I'M JUST GLAD WE'VE GOT HIM INSTEAD OF THAT STUCK-UP *DRAGON WOMAN.*

OH, MACLEOD? YEAH, SHE'S A RIGHT *BITCH.*

!!

WHAT?! SHE IS *NOT!* SHE'S A *GENIUS!* SHE'S WHY I'M EVEN *HERE!* SHE'S AN *INSPIRATION!!*

YOU CAN OGLE PROFESSOR PIERCE'S *BOTTOM* ALL YOU LIKE BUT I WILL *NOT* HAVE YOU—

AHEM

IF, UH, WE COULD QUIETEN DOWN PLEASE, ISABELLA? THEN I CAN BEGIN... THANK YOU.

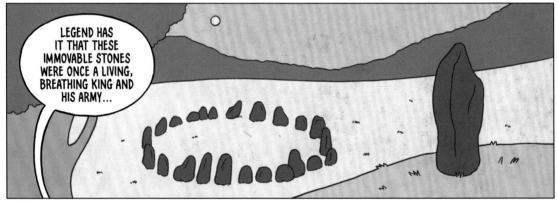

THEY MARCHED ON PEACEFULLY UNTIL THEIR WAY WAS BARRED BY AN UGLY OLD WITCH, WHO HAD GREEDILY CLAIMED THE TERRITORY ACROSS WHICH OUR HEROES NEEDED TO TRAVERSE.

THE WITCH SPAT AN EVIL CURSE AT THE KING:

SEVEN LONG STRIDES SHALT THOU TAKE, AND IF LONG COMPTON THOU CANST SEE, KING OF ENGLAND THOU SHALT BE!

THE JUST AND COURAGEOUS KING HAD NO CHOICE BUT TO TAKE HIS SEVEN STEPS, ALTHOUGH HE KNEW ALL TOO WELL THAT THE HUGE HILLOCK THAT LAY JUST BEFORE THE EDGE OF THE VALLEY, WOULD PREVENT HIM FROM SEEING THE VILLAGE.

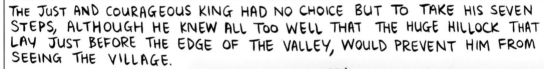

HIS KNIGHTS BEHIND HIM WERE WHISPERING TO EACH OTHER IN AWE AT THE KING'S BRAVERY, WHEN THE WITCH'S CURSE TURNED THEM ALL TO-

RUMBLE...

I'S DUNNAE LIKE BEIN' INTERRUPTED, LASS...

OK I'M SORRY! LOOK, JUST... WHAT DO YOU *WANT* FROM ME? I'M *NOBODY!*

I NE'ER KNO WHATE WOLL PLEASE THEE ABOUT A LASS UNTIL IT COME ABOUT, DEARIE.

WHAT DOES *THAT* MEAN?! *PLEASE* YOU?! OH MY GOSH, THIS IS CRAZY! I'M GOING *CRAZY!! AAAAAARGH!!*

ACH, VEREE WEL, LITTLE BEAST. BLODWEN SHALL FREE YON FROM HER CURSE...

BUT SHE'LL BE HAVING SOME *PLAYE* WITH THEM BEFOREWHYLE...

W-WAIT, WHAT?

AAHAHAHAHAHAA!!

LIFT

PUT

STAND

PUSH

GRAB

GRAB

STACK

READEE, LITTLE **BEAST**?

WAIT! I...

//cLICk!//

SLAM!

stal packaging

WET FLOOR

SQUELCH! SQUELCH! SQUELCH!

I WISH TO BUY THIS JIFFY BAG... *THANK YOU...*

WHATE IS THOU DOING? THOU MON NOT DO THATE!

I'M POSTING THIS BOTTLE BACK TO THE MUSEUM! DON'T TRY TO STOP ME! I'VE MADE MY DECISION, EVIL WITCH!

IT'S A PLAN THAT NOT EVEN YOU CAN MESS UP!

TEN MINUTES LATER...

THANK YOU!

CLOSED FOR RENOVATIONS

AHAHAHA HAHAHAHAHAHA HAHAHAA!!

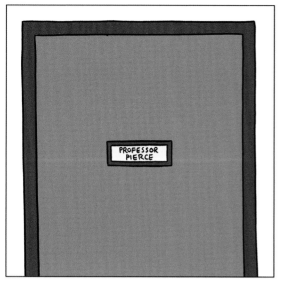

SIGH
COME ON NOW...

KNOCK
KNOCK

COME IN!

UM...
SORRY TO–

AH! ISABELLA,
IS THAT YOU?

I WAS JUST–
OH! YOUR CLOTHES
ARE ALL WET! WHAT
ON EARTH...ARE
YOU OK?

I'M FINE,
PROFESSOR...
I JUST...

...FANCIED
A CHAT?

BY ALL MEANS!
I'LL GET YOU A TOWEL
AND MAKE US SOME
HOT TEA, EH?

SO NOW YOU'RE ALL DRIED OFF, WAS THERE SOMETHING YOU WANTED TO TALK ABOUT?

OH, I JUST WANTED SOME COMPANY REALLY...UM, BUT MAYBE WE COULD CHAT ABOUT THE STORY FROM TODAY'S LECTURE?

LONG COMPTON? AHH, WELL NOW *THERE'S* AN INTERESTING PLACE—

HMM, MAYBE NOT SO MUCH THE *LOCATION* OF THE TALE...

THE KING? I'M AFRAID I DON'T KNOW EXACTLY WHERE HE WAS CROWNED BUT THERE IS—

UH, YES, I DON'T THINK I NEED TO KNOW ANYMORE ABOUT THE KING HIM*SELF*...

AND, UH, I FEEL QUITE KNOWLEDGEABLE ABOUT THE KNIGHTS, TOO. PRETTY SIMPLE MOTIVATION *THERE*, HAHA!

'SILENT DISCO, FOAM...PARTY...' OOOO!

LISTEN...

...BLODWEN?

I'M SENSING THAT, FOR SOME REASON, YOU DON'T WANT TO LEAVE.

I MON STAY UNTIL I AM PLEASED. *SATISFIED.*

BUT YOU NEED TO TELL ME WHAT THAT *MEANS.*

I DON'T *KNO* WHAT IT MEANS.

THE THING IS... YOU'RE MAKING IT VERY HARD FOR—

KNOK KNOK!

IT'S 9.15! WHAT ON *EARTH* HAPPENED TO MY *ALARM?!*

IT WAS A WICKED, NASTEE NOISE, SO I *STRUCK* IT!

YOU RUDDY *SWITCHED IT OFF!* I'M GOING TO BE LATE TO MY FIRST LECTURE NOW!

OH, DO NOT FRET. THEY WOLL SOON FORGET YOUR LATENESS ONCE I ARRIVE...

W-WHAT DO YOU MEAN?

WHERE'D YOU GET ALL THESE COUPONS, BLODWEN? MINE RAN OUT *YONKS* AGO.

FROM ISABELLA'S **BIN!**

FIGURES.

HEY BLODWEN! LIBBY AND ME ARE GONNA SHARE A BOTTLE. YOU WANT IN?

NO!!

AH, A *WINE* BOTTLE...UH, NO THANK YOU. I WOLL HAVE THE TWO HUNDERED AND FORTY ONE COCKTAILS.

UM.

WHAT?

OH! HAHA! **DUH!** VERY FUNNY, BLODWEN.

RIIIGHT. TWO MORE SEX ON THE SOFAS, THEN.

HMM. WOLL I *SUPPOSE* I CUD DRINK THEM TWO AT A TIME...

I'LL GET THESE, GIRLS, YOU SIT DOWN. ISABELLA COULD YOU HELP ME?

OH, SURE.

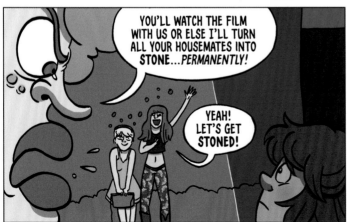

CALL THAT A DEVIL!? I'S SEEN SCARIER *SQUIRRELS!*

HAHAHAHAA!

ME AND MY MATES WATCHED THIS YEARS AGO WHEN MY DAD WAS OUT...SCARED US SHITLESS!

THIS IS A CLASSIC! I THINK ISABELLA'S SCARED THOUGH...!

I'M NOT SCARED...JUST *TIRED.*

POOOR BAAAABY!

THAT WAS AMAZING! I'VE BEEN WANTING A NIGHT LIKE THAT FOR *DECADES!*

YOU MON ADMIT IT WAS MERRY. YOU ENJOYED YOURSELF, EH?

YOU HAVE A *GIFT* FOR READING PEOPLE, BLODWEN. I'VE NEVER BEEN SO GLAD TO SEE MY BED.

BEFORE YOU SLUMBER LET US DISCUSS WHAT WE'LL DO ON THE MORROW! LIBBY GAVE ME THIS 'FLYER' FOR SOMETHING CALLED A 'FOAM PARTEE'!

NO!

NO! NO! **NO!** I HELD UP MY END OF THE DEAL – AND THEN SOME! YOU HAVE TO LEAVE ME THE HECK ALONE NOW!

BUT WE COULD HAVE SO MUCH MORE MERRYMENT! YOU ARE SUCH A SOGGY CABBAGE!

THAT'S...NOT A **THING!** AND NONE OF THIS WAS 'MERRY' FOR *ME!* I'M NOT LIKE OTHER GIRLS!

WOLL, **DUH.** ALL GIRLS ARE *LITERALLY* ALL DIFFERENT ONES.

NOW *YOU* NEED TO GO AWAY, AND *I* NEED TO–

GAAAAAARGH!!

I KNEW YOU WOULD BE EXCITED!

WHAT THE *HELL* IS THAT BOY DOING IN MY *BED??* DID *YOU* DO THIS??

DON'T WORRY, HE'S NOT HURT! AND HE WOLL AWAKEN AS SOON AS I CLICK MY FINGERS—

DON'T YOU *DARE!*

OH MY GOD! OH MY GOD! I'M NOT EVEN SUPPOSED TO HAVE BOYS IN HERE! OH MY GOD!

I THOUGHT IT WOULD BE MERRY! HE'D BE A GOOD COMPANION FOR YOU!

STOP TALKING! SHUT UP! SHUT UP AND GET HIM OUT OF HERE *NOW!!*

≡ POOF! ≡

"SHUT UP" YOU SAY?

FINE.

I WOLL MAKE THINGS VERY QUIET FOR YOU...

WAIT! WHAT ARE Y–

Oferhlēoðura! Þu hlystest āngilde þá hwa gieman ymbutan þu! Hlysnen: Oferhlēoðura!!

BANG

AH! MORNIN', ISSY!

HELLO. UM. YOU TWO LOOK *AWFUL.*

OH, LEAVE OFF HER, MANDY. ISSY'S PROBABLY JUST WORRIED ABOUT HOW POORLY YOU LOOK.

LIBBY!!

HEY, ISABELLA!

UGH! DON'T COME OVER, DON'T COME OVER...

HE'S STAYING WITH HIS FRIENDS...THANK GOODNESS.

AT LEAST HE DOESN'T SEEM TO REMEMBER ANYTHING ABOUT LAST NIGHT...

45 USELESS MINUTES LATER...

OK, OK...DON'T PANIC. THIS IS FINE. YOU CAN WORK THIS OUT.

YOU'RE THE CLEVEREST PERSON I KNOW.

WHAT WAS IT THAT BLODWEN SAID WHEN SHE THREW ALL THAT RED MIST AT ME?

OFERHLEODURA...PU HLYSTEST ...ANGILL? PA HWA GIEMAN... SOMETHING...THEN OFERHLEODURA AGAIN...GOSH THIS IS REALLY BROKEN OLD ENGLISH...

OFERHLEODURA MEANS...'FAILURE TO LISTEN'? OR 'FAILURE TO HEAR'? WELL, THAT SOUNDS RIGHT...

GIEMAN MEANS 'TO CARE'...PU IS 'YOU', I THINK. SO, 'ME'.

TWENTY MINUTES LATER...

SO..I CAN ONLY HEAR PEOPLE IF THEY CARE ABOUT ME? OK, WELL, THAT FITS I GUESS.

IN THAT CASE I HAVE TWO OPTIONS: FIND BLODWEN AND GET HER TO REVERSE THIS CURSE, *OR* GET MORE THAN TWO PEOPLE TO CARE ABOUT ME...

nd Blodwen and get r to reverse the curse
:OR:
. Get more than <u>two</u> <u>people</u> to care about me.

ura #

NO! *I* KNOW WHAT TO DO!

HE DEFINITELY CARES ABOUT ME FOR *SURE*.

AND HIS DOOR IS *ALWAYS* OPEN!

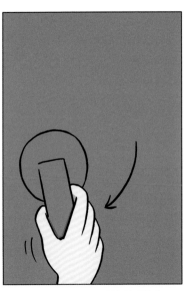

NO...

NO, NO , NO, THIS CAN'T BE RIGHT...

I...I MUST HAVE GOT THE RULES WRONG, THERE'S NO WAY PROFESSOR PIERCE DOESN'T CARE ABOUT ME...HE'S THE ONLY REAL FRIEND I-I...

I MUST HAVE GOT THE CURSE WRONG...

..MAYBE IT'S THE COMPLETE OPPOSITE...

..I MEAN...HE *CLEARLY* CARES.

SIP

SHUFF

GET OFF ME!

SNIFF

O COME NOW, IT IS NOT *THAT* BAD A CURSE!

I'S GOT MUCH *WORSE* ONES I COULD HAVE USED!

LEAVE ME ALONE...

IT...*IS* THE CURSE YOU'RE UPSET ABOUT, EY?

LEAVE ME ALONE.

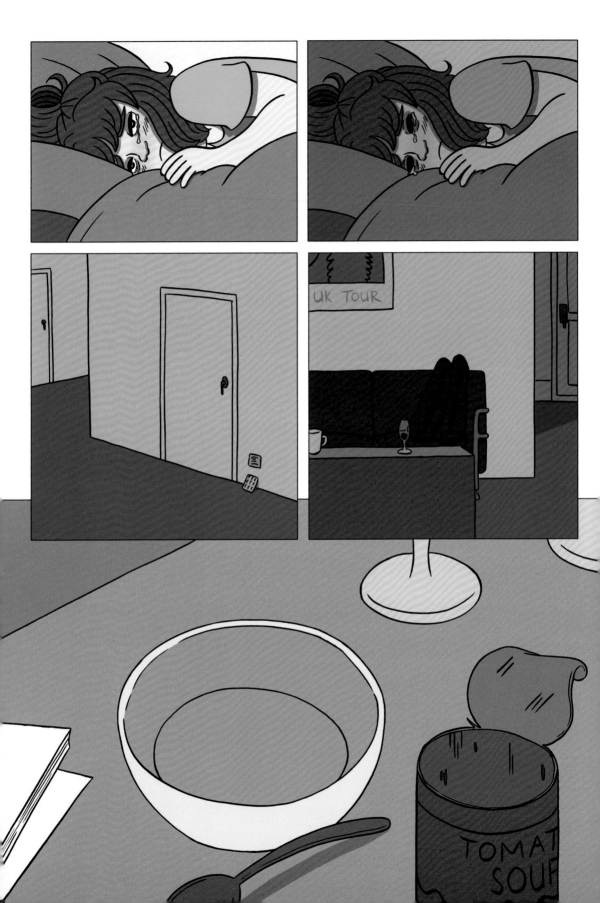

SO.

I THINK WE GOT OFF TO A BAD START—

UM! YEAH! UNDERSTATEMENT OF THE *CENTURY*, BLODWEN!

URRRGHHHHHH...

I THINK I SHOULD TELL THEE A LITTLE ABOUT ...MY...SELF.

WIGGLE WIGGLE

AND I SHOULD — WHAT ARE YOU DOING?

I'M BECOMING A BURRITO.

WIGGLE

EXAMT

I LIKE YOU AS A BURRITO!

TELL THE STORY, BLODWEN.

I WAS A VERY TALENTED HEALER. I FIRST PRACTISED MEDICINE 370 YEARS PAST.

I WAS GIFTED WITH POTIONS AND VERY POWERFUL...BUT RATHER THAN REVERED, I WAS PROCLAIMED A WITCH AND A THREAT.

I WAS PUNISHED AND DEMONISED BY MEN BECAUSE THEY DIDN'T UNDERSTAND MY TALENTS.

THEY TRIED TO BURN ME MANY TIMES.

I ALWAYS ESCAPED.

BUT EACH TIME THE WOUNDS CUT DEEPER.

WOMEN HAVE ALWAYS BEEN DEMONISED BY MEN IF THEY BECOME TOO CLEVER OR POWERFUL OR ABLE TO DO THINGS THAT MEN CANNOT.

YET WE ARE THE ONES PUNISHED. NOT THEM.

THAT'S NOT *ALWAYS* TRUE. BESIDES: YOU ARE A *BIT* OF A THREAT! YOU TURNED EVERYONE TO **STONE** THE DAY I MET YOU!

I ONLY DID THAT TO SNAP YOU OUT OF YOUR SELFISH STUPOR. THAT'S HALF THE REASON HARDLY ANYONE LIKES YOU, YOU KNOW.

WH..WELL, WHAT'S THE *OTHER* HALF...?

YOU'RE TOO CLEVER. PEOPLE RESENT YOU. EXACTLY THE *SAME* AS THEY RESENTED ME, ONLY CENTURIES LATER.

WHEN YOU FIRST MET ME...YOU THOUGHT I WAS LIKE THE PEOPLE WHO DEMONISED YOU, DIDN'T YOU? LIKE THOSE MEN.

NO, BUT I THOUGHT YOU WOULD GROW UP TO BE LIKE THEM.

YOU ARE AMBITIOUS AND SELFISH, BUT YOU ARE ALSO INCREDIBLY LONELY AND OVERWHELMED.

I'M *NOT* OVERWHELMED! WHY DO PEOPLE KEEP **SAYING** THAT?

SHHHHH...MY GOODNESS, IT IS *SO* EASY TO GET UNDER YOUR GOAT!

S-SKIN!

GET SOME SLEEP. WE WILL GO FOR A WALK ON THE MORROW.

THAT WILL BE NICE, YES?

I WANT TO TELL YOU THE **TRUE** VERSION OF THE STORY THAT *PIG* WAS TELLING YOU IN HIS BIG, FANCY LECTURE HALL.

ARE YOU READY TO LEAVE THIS FOOTPATH AND TRAVEL TO A TINY VILLAGE NAMED LONG COMPTON?!

IN THIS TINY VILLAGE WE WILL FIND THE ROLLRIGHT STONES. A GROUP OF NEOLITHIC STONE MONUMENTS KNOWN AS – THE KING STONE, THE WHISPERING KNIGHTS, AND THE KINGMAN STONE CIRCLE.

THESE STONES, BELIEVE IT OR NOT, WERE ONCE A LIVING, BREATHING KING AND HIS ARMY.

THE KING WAS HELL-BENT ON SEIZING ALL THE LAND HE COULD.

HIS CONQUEST EVENTUALLY LED HIM TO LONG COMPTON.

JUST BEFORE THEY CRESTED THE BROW THE KING MET A WOMAN. A GIFTED HERBALIST, WHO HELD THE TERRITORY ACROSS WHICH THE ARMY WAS MARCHING.

WAIT, THE PLACE THE KING AND HIS ARMY WERE MARCHING THROUGH ALREADY BELONGED TO THE WITCH? PROFESSOR PIERCE SAID THE WITCH HAD 'GREEDILY CLAIMED' IT FOR HERSELF!

YOUR PROFESSOR IS FULL OF SHIT. DON'T INTERRUPT ME.

THE WITCH PROPHESIED TO THE KING:

SEVEN LONG STRIDES SHALT THOU TAKE, AND IF LONG COMPTON THOU CANST SEE, KING OF ENGLAND THOU SHALT BE!

THE ARROGANT KING, WHO WAS CERTAIN HE WAS ALMOST AT THE TOP OF THE HILL REPLIED, FATALLY:

STICK, STOCK, STONE, AS KING OF ENGLAND I SHALL BE KNOWN!

AND HE TOOK SEVEN LONG STRIDES FORWARD.

BUT THE IGNORANT KING HAD NOT ANTICIPATED THE LONG MOUND OF EARTH THAT LAY BEFORE THE EDGE OF THE SLOPE.

HE COULD NOT SEE THE VILLAGE.

AND SINCE HE HAD FAILED, THE WITCH TURNED HIM INTO THE VERY STONE THAT HE HAD SWORN BY HIS VOW.

THE WHISPERING KNIGHTS BEHIND HIM WERE NOT IN AWE OF THE KING'S BRAVERY, BUT RATHER PLOTTING MUTINY AND REBELLION TO OVERTHROW THEIR OVERWEENING LEADER.

SO YOU SEE, DEARIE, IT WAS THE KING, IN THE TALE, WHO WAS ARROGANT AND GREEDY. THE WITCH WAS MERELY CARRYING OUT THE DEED THAT *HE HIMSELF* BOASTED ABOUT.

I SUPPOSE YOU'RE ALSO GOING TO TELL ME THE TALE IS ABOUT MAN'S AMBITION AND ENTITLEMENT, AND ABOUT WOMEN RESISTING THAT...

EXACTLY.

NOW I SHALL TELL YOU OF THE GOBLIN MARKET!

NO, HANG ON! PIERCE ALSO TOLD ME A STORY ABOUT HOW TWO WITCHES ONCE DRAGGED A MAN OUT OF HIS HOUSE AND LEFT HIM TO DIE AT THE TOP OF A TREE! IS *THAT* TRUE?

SOME OF IT, YES...DID HE MENTION THAT THE TWO WITCHES WERE SISTERS, AND THAT THE MAN THEY PUT IN THE TREE HAD BEEN MAKING LOVE TO BOTH OF THEM, BEHIND EACH SISTER'S BACK?

N- NO!

BESIDES, THE MAN DIDN'T *DIE.* HE WAS JUST *FOUND HALF DEAD* THE NEXT DAY. BIG DIFFERENCE!

I WILL HELP YOU WITH THIS PIERCE MAN, AND WITH THIS INTERN SHIP...IF YOU WISH?

YOU REMEMBERED ABOUT THAT?

BUT YOU NEED TO DO SOMETHING FOR *ME* IN RETURN...

NO! NO MORE CLUBBING! I CAN'T DO IT! PLEASE!

I WON'T MAKE YOU DO ANYTHING YOU DON'T WANT TO DO ANYMORE. I JUST...WANT YOU TO TRY TO RELAX A LITTLE. HAVE SOME FUN. WHATEVER THAT MEANS FOR YOU...OK?

OH. UM... I CAN TRY MY BEST...

THE NEXT DAY I TOOK MYSELF TO THE MODERN ART GALLERY. I'D NEVER BEEN BEFORE.

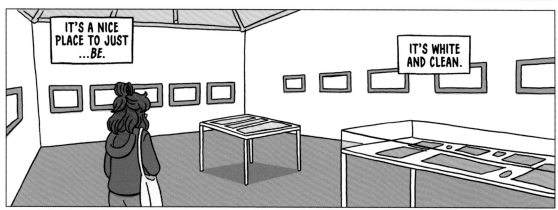

IT'S A NICE PLACE TO JUST ...*BE.*

IT'S WHITE AND CLEAN.

AND IT'S *QUIET.*

GAAARGH!

LADY ISABEL IS VISITED BY THE HANDSOME ELF-KNIGHT. HE PERSUADES HER TO ACCOMPANY HIM ON A RIDE INTO THE GREENWOODS.

AFTER A FEW MINUTES HE THROWS HER OFF THE HORSE. HE INTENDS TO THROW HER OFF A CLIFF OVERLOOKING THE SEA. A PLACE WHERE HE HAS ALREADY DROWNED SEVEN OTHER WOMEN.

THE ELF-KNIGHT COMMANDS ISABEL TO UNDRESS; HE WISHES TO SELL HER FINE CLOTHES ONCE SHE IS DEAD. ISABEL AGREES AS LONG AS HE TURN HIS BACK TO RESPECT HER MODESTY.

AS SOON AS THE ELF-KNIGHT TURNS, ISABEL THROWS HIM OFF THE CLIFF AND INTO THE SEA!

IT'S ALL COORDINATED BY DUMB *STUDENTS.* IT'S NOT EVEN GOT *ADULTS* RUNNING IT...

EXACTLY! AND WOULDN'T IT BE A VERY USEFUL AND REWARDING EXTRA-CURRICULAR ACTIVITY TO TAKE THE PLACE OF THE WORK YOU WERE DOING FOR A CERTAIN HORRID AND CREEPY PROFESSOR...?

UUUUGGGHHH...

OH COME ON! I SPENT AGES COMING UP WITH THAT *VERY GOOD PLAN!* WON'T YOU EVEN TRY IT??

WHAT IF I GET *BUDDIED UP* WITH SOMEONE **AWFUL**, THOUGH?

OHH YOU'LL BE WITH SOMEONE **GREAT**! JUST LEAVE THAT TO ME! I HAVE A FEW TRICKS UP MY TROUSERS!

THAT'S NOT— URGH! FINE! I'LL TRY IT...

GOOD 'CAUSE YOU'RE SUPPOSED TO MEET WITH THE TEAM LEADER IN FIVE MINUTES...

WHAT?!

IT'S NOTHING, I'VE GOTTEN A LOT WORSE FROM PARENTS, BELIEVE ME. I TOLD YOUR AUNT I WAS HERE AND SHE SAID YOU'D BE RIGHT ALONG!

WE LIKE THAT SORT OF SPIRIT HERE AT THE STUDENT BUDDY SCHEME. THAT'S WHY I HAVE MY TRUSTY BRIEFCASE FULL OF FILES ON ME AT ALL TIMES.

ALWAYS BE PREPARED: THAT'S MY MOTTO!

AAARGH!

I BEG YOUR PARDON?

UH! AAARGH – AAA – A COMMENDABLE ATTITUDE! VERY COMMENDABLE!

HM. WELL, THANKS.

SHOVE!

OH, CLUMSY ME!

CRUMBS, ONE OF THOSE ENVELOPES IS YOUR MATCH! I RAN SOME ALGORITHMS AND MATCHED YOU UP ALREADY. HOPE YOU DON'T MIND.

HEE HEE!

NOT AT ALL. VERY EFFICIENT!

THE SPELL TO PUT SOMEONE INTO A DREAMLESS SLEEP TAKES A WHILE, SO I HAD TIME TO LOOK AROUND...

IT TOOK ALL OF MY STEALTH AND DEDUCTION SKILLS..

BUT I SOON FIGURED OUT THE SUBTLE CLUES.

MACLEOD
SHAUN
BRITISH CITIZEN
22 MAR / MARS
M

...

OH MY GOD! HE INVITED ME TO DINNER WITH HIM AND HIS *MUM!* I SAID *NO!* I COULD HAVE HAD DINNER WITH THE GREAT *PROFESSOR MACLEOD AT HER HOME!!*

YOU MIGHT STILL HAVE YOUR CHANCE! YOU WANT THIS INTERN-SHIP BUT DON'T WANT TO WORK WITH PIERCE ANYMORE..MAYBE SHAUN COULD PUT IN A GOOD WORD...?

AND YOU'D STILL BE DOING EXTRA CURRICULAR THINGS WITH HIM!

THAT WAY WE'RE KILLING *TWO FISH WITH ONE BARREL!*

OH MY GOD! THAT WAS...YOUR WORST ONE YET!

TWO FISH ONE...CUP?

AARGH!!

HEY! IS EVERYTHIN-

ISABELLA'S GETTING READY FOR A **DATE!**

I AM NOT! I'M JUST GOING TO **TALK** TO A **FRIEND!** AND BLODWEN HAS THE **WORST** TASTE IN FASHION!

I...MIGHT BE ABLE TO HELP HERE..

WOW, I LOOK... NICE!

YOU JUST NEEDED A BIT OF T.L.C! YOU'VE SEEMED A BIT STRESSED LATELY AND IT WAS STARTING TO SHOW. NO OFFENCE!

NOW YOU LOOK LIKE YOU'RE BACK TO YOUR GOOD OLD SELF!

MEH.

HOW DID YOU GET SO GOOD AT THIS?

I'VE ALWAYS LOVED CLOTHES. I'D LIKE TO BE A FASHION JOURNALIST ONE DAY...IT'S A DREAM...

I ALMOST DIDN'T COME TO OXFORD. I GOT A SCHOLARSHIP AT THE LAST MINUTE.

OH, GOSH! THAT'S VERY IMPRESSIVE, ANNIE.

AW, THANKS, MATE. IT'S ONLY 'CAUSE MY FOLKS DON'T HAVE MUCH MONEY!

AND BECAUSE YOU HAVE GREAT POTENTIAL!

OH, SHUSH!

HELLO, SHAUN.

OH, HEY! YOU'RE MY STUDENT BUDDY, ARE YOU?

YES. SHOULD BE A NICE DAY.

THAT'S THE SPIRIT!

SO, UH, WHILE WE'RE WAITING FOR THE BUS...CAN I ASK YOU SOMETHING?

SURE...

WELL, YOU MENTIONED YOUR MUM THE OTHER DAY...AND I HEARD THAT SHE—

OH.

YOU'VE WORKED IT OUT HAVE YOU? THERE'S ME THINKING YOU'D ACTUALLY DECIDED TO BE *NICE*.

UH OH...

YOU KNOW THAT MY MUM IS PROFESSOR MACLEOD AND *SUDDENLY* YOU'RE INTERESTED IN HANGING OUT WITH ME?

UH OH!!

YOU KNOW WHAT? I WAS ACTUALLY GOING TO RECOMMEND YOU FOR MY MUM'S INTERNSHIP...BUT MAYBE YOU'D BE BETTER OFF GOING HOME TO YOUR FOLKS.

YOU COMIN' OR GOIN', LOVE?

HOP.

SHAUN, LISTEN...I NEVER MEANT—

WHILST I APPRECIATE YOUR ENTHUSIASM, I'D REALLY RATHER RIDE THE BUS IN *SILENCE.*

R— RIGHT!

UHH... *SHAUN?*

YOU'RE GOING TO HAVE TO TALK TO ME JUST FOR A SECOND TO TELL ME WHAT WE'RE LOOKING FOR...?

SHOVE

OH. RIGHT.

11.00AM

12.30PM

2.00PM

3.45PM

5.10PM

SIGH

SO BLODWEN'S PLAN FAILED. AND SHAUN HATES ME.

SOD IT. SOD THEM. I CAN SORT THIS OUT BY MYSELF.

I'VE ALWAYS SORTED THINGS OUT BY MYSELF.

THERE MUST BE SOMEONE I CAN REPORT PIERCE TO. HIS BEHAVIOUR WAS *UNACCEPTABLE.*

IF I DON'T SAY SOMETHING...IT MIGHT HAPPEN TO SOMEONE ELSE.

I AM ISABELLA MARIA PENWICK-WICKAM.

AND I CAN *CRACK* THIS!

that boys' club-type treatment, it ome as no surprise to learn that the student's abuser remains on campus s job still intact. The university has not cided the case, even though the scho ped its investigation three months ag n asked what they were waiting for, a kesperson told us they were unable to nment.

The truth rema harassment universities, but means risking y

A lecturer has been convicted attacking his student. He pu face, knocking her out, and s court heard. She was left wi and bruises on her side in a she said changed her life. H er of salt in her face chippin causing her nose to bleed. I between his arrest and sent to teach at the university.

A professor of feminist studies resigned from her university po in protest over the alleged sexua harassment of students by staff. She said that the inquiries had n led to a robust or meaningful investigation of alleged problems at the institution.

A student at the instituti Tuesday that a football school raped her in Feb the university has done about it, despite the fac all the right avenues in administrators and auth

"I can confidently say that the worst things I have seen and experienced happened when male senior academics were in charge all the way to the top of the hierarchy."

s: sexual
rife in
mplaining
r career.

spoke to the right people,)
all has been done. This is now 6 month

The inappropriate comments and the
unreasonable requests (and worse) all
stem from a system where many, man
men are now safely established in
permanent posts.

The investigators provided reassuranc
when my abuser became upset, they
even laughed with him.

not want to be here anym

violently
ed her in
ped on
black e
eal whi
ew a co
r tooth
ten m
he cor

**Questions to the victim from the
authorities included:**

"What was I wearing?"
"What was I drinking?"
"How much did I drink?"
"What time did I start drinking?"
"How much did I eat that day?"
"Did I lead him on?"
"Had I hooked up with him before?"
"Do I often have one night stands?"
"Did I even say no?"
"What is my sexual history?"
"How many men have I slept with?"
"Had I

leged
r at the
and that
to nothing
she used
ming both
es.

ooked up with him b
en have one night s
Did I even say no?
at is my sexual hist
any men have I sle

THAT'S IT.

I'VE LOST EVERYTHING.

MY CHANCE AT THE INTERNSHIP...

MY PLACE AT THE UNIVERSITY...

...AND SHAUN.

TRUST ME. IT'LL BE WORTH IT. I HAVE LOTS OF IDEAS ON HOW TO WORK THIS OUT.

Y-YOU'LL REALLY HELP ME...?

YES!

...IF YOU'LL DO SOMETHING FOR *ME* IN RETURN...

NO, BLODWEN! I'M *NOT* GOING CLUBBING AGAIN! I *HATED* IT! AND IT GOT ME INTO TROUBLE WITH SHAUN! AND-

SHHHHHHHHHHHH! NO, NO, LISTEN:

I KNOW YOU HATE CLUBBING - I KNOW THAT NOW! I JUST WANT TO HANG OUT WITH PEOPLE! JUST SOME NIGHTS IN WITH ANNIE WATCHING FILMS. *YOU* CAN EVEN PICK THE FILMS!

HM. THAT SOUNDS ALRIGHT I GUESS...

WHAT ABOUT AMANDA AND LIBBY? YOU ALL SEEMED TO GET ALONG AT THE CLUB.

NAH. THEY'RE DICKS.

IF THAT PLANE LEAVES THE GROUND AND YOU'RE NOT WITH HIM, YOU'LL REGRET IT.

MAYBE NOT TODAY...

MAYBE NOT TOMORROW...

BUT SOON, AND FOR THE REST OF YOUR LIFE.

AWW, THAT WAS WELL NICE! GOOD CHOICE, ISSY!

SO, DEEP DOWN THE LITTLE BEAST IS A *ROMANTIC!*

LEAVE ME ALONE! SHALL WE WATCH ANOHER ONE?

OOH, YEAH!

ABSOLUTELY NOT! ISABELLA NEEDS TO BE UP EARLY FOR HER SECOND STUDENT BUDDY DATE!

UUGH! IT'S NOT A DATE! AND HE DOESN'T WANT ME THERE! I'M NOT GOING!

OH NO, ISABELLA, YOU SHOULD GO! IT'LL BE REALLY GOOD EXPERIENCE.

HMMMM... I'LL THINK ABOUT IT.

GO FOR *ME*, WON'T YOU? BESIDES, IT'LL BE *WELL* NICE TO SPEND TOMORROW OUTSIDE – THE WEATHER'S MEANT TO BE *GORGEOUS!*

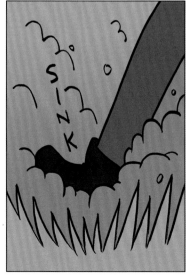

ISABELLA??

ISABELLA! ARE YOU--?

ARE THESE-

PANT

-THE RIGHT ONES?

NO...

OH.

PFFF-HAHA!

HAHAHA HAHA!

I WAS REALLY RUDE TO YOU WHEN WE FIRST MET. I'M SORRY.

IT'S OK, I WAS PRETTY HORRIBLE TO YOU AFTER THAT.

NO, I DESERVED IT. I DIDN'T DESERVE YOU TO BE SO NICE TO ME IN THE FIRST PLACE.

MUM WANTED ME TO KEEP AN EYE ON YOU 'CAUSE OF YOUR AGE...AND...I JUST LIKED HOW YOU WERE DIFFERENT FROM OTHER GIRLS, YOU KNOW?

NO GIRL IS *LIKE THE OTHERS*, SHAUN. WE'RE ALL DIFFERENT ONES.

OH, I DIDN'T MEAN-! WAIT...I WAS JUST SAYING WHAT *YOU* SAID A FEW DAYS AGO!

I KNOW! I KNOW!

I WAS AN IDIOT BACK THEN.

2016 UK TOUR

A FEW DAYS LATER...

WELL, IT'S STARTING TO LOOK LIKE I'M NOT GETTING EXPELLED AFTER ALL..

SURELY SOMETHING WOULD HAVE HAPPENED BY NOW, OR SHAUN WOULD HAVE SAID SOMETHING...RIGHT?

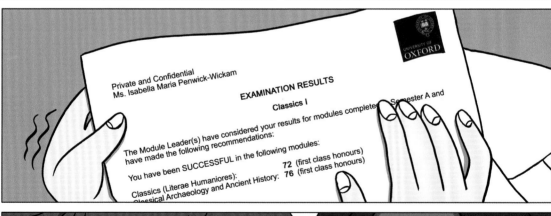

I GAVE YOU A CHANCE AT THIS UNIVERSITY BECAUSE, DESPITE YOUR AGE, YOU HAVE MADE OUTSTANDING ACADEMIC ACHIEVEMENTS AND POSSESS AN IMPRESSIVE MATURITY.

THANK YOU.

SORRY.

IMAGINE MY SURPRISE, THEN, TO LEARN THAT YOU HAVE BEEN SEEN IN BARS AND CLUBS LATE AT NIGHT. I AM PLEASED YOU HAVE MADE FRIENDS HERE, MS. PENWICK-WICKAM BUT YOU ARE *UNDERAGE*. I AM NOT A FAN OF STUDENTS BREAKING THE RULES, MUCH LESS THE *LAW*.

AND SO...

SO I'VE BEEN THINKING I SHOULD – –

YOU CAN STAY HERE, YOU KNOW. YOU'RE VERY WELCOME.

THANKS, BUT I'M MORE THAN PLEASED WITH YOU. ONCE I'M SATISFIED IT'S AWAYS BEST THAT I...MOVE ON.

RIGHT.

I HEARD THE MUSEUM WAS OPEN AGAIN.

YES, I THINK IT IS.

THE GOBLIN MARKET

Two sisters, Lizzie and Laura, live together in a little cottage and lead quiet, wholesome lives.

But each evening they hear the cries of the goblin fruit sellers.

These goblins come out of the forest towards the cottage, offering all kinds of ripe fruit...

...from sharp wild free-born cranberries to bloom-down-cheek'd peaches...

...even pomegranates, melons, and figs to fill your mouth.

LIZZIE REFUSES, IGNORING THESE OMINOUS MERCHANTS.

BUT LAURA IS CURIOUS, AND STAYS TO LOOK AT THE STRANGE LITTLE MEN.

ONE NIGHT, LAURA BUYS SOME FRUIT FROM THE GOBLINS WITH A LOCK OF HER GOLDEN HAIR.

AND RIGHT AWAY SHE IS GOBBLING IT DOWN AS IF SHE IS A GOBLIN HERSELF.

LIZZIE WARNED HER SISTER THAT THEY DID NOT KNOW ENOUGH ABOUT THE SINISTER FRUIT, OR THE MENACING FRUIT SELLERS, TO RISK EATING IT.

SHE TELLS OF ANOTHER MAIDEN WHO ATE THE GOBLIN'S WARES, THEN PINED AWAY AND DIED OF SORROW.

ONCE A MAIDEN HAS GIVEN IN TO THE GOBLIN SELLERS' TEMPTATIONS, SHE CAN NO LONGER SEE OR HEAR THEM. SHE HAS GROWN ADDICTED TO THE SWEET FRUIT BUT IS NEVER GIVEN ANOTHER CHANCE TO TASTE IT.

AND SO LAURA IS HAUNTED BY THE FRUIT WHICH IS NOW BEYOND HER REACH. SHE CAN THINK OF NOTHING ELSE.

LIZZIE VOWS TO HELP HER DYING SISTER. SHE VISITS THE GOBLINS.

DESPITE THEM BEATING AND TAUNTING HER, LIZZIE REFUSES TO TASTE EVEN A MORSEL OF THE GOBLINS' FRUIT,

SHE COMES HOME COVERED WITH THE JUICE OF THEIR WARES, WHICH LAURA RAVENOUSLY LICKS FROM HER FACE.

THIS "FIERY ANTIDOTE", ONCE SO SWEET AND DESIRABLE, NOW TASTES AS BITTER AS "WORMWOOD TO HER TONGUE."

BUT THE ADDICTION HAS BEEN CURED, AND AFTER A FEVERED NIGHT LAURA WAKES UP HEALTHY AND BACK TO HER OLD SELF ONCE MORE

I THINK I UNDERSTAND.

OH YES?

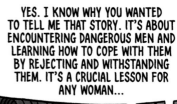

YES. I KNOW WHY YOU WANTED TO TELL ME THAT STORY. IT'S ABOUT ENCOUNTERING DANGEROUS MEN AND LEARNING HOW TO COPE WITH THEM BY REJECTING AND WITHSTANDING THEM. IT'S A CRUCIAL LESSON FOR ANY WOMAN...

FOR ME.

MY, AREN'T WE *STUDIOUS!*

YOU'VE ONLY *JUST* NOTICED?

WELL, NOW, THAT'S SOME GOOD ANALYSIS THERE... BUT YOU'VE MISSED ONE VERY IMPORTANT LESSON.

THERE IS NO FRIEND LIKE A SISTER.

AH!

HELLO, YOU TWO!

OOH! WHAT LOVELY FLOWERS!

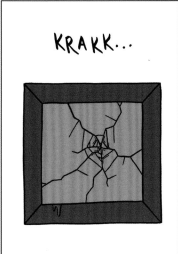

Acknowledgements

This book has had the most ridiculous journey from concept to publication, so special thanks must be given to Lizzie Kaye for believing in it enough to offer it a home not once, but twice. Thank you to my partner, Rob, for supporting me throughout its creation, and to my mum, Hazel, for bringing me up to be the intensely curious, museum-loving comic creator that I am. Speaking of museums, thank you to the Pitt Rivers Museum for keeping my favourite artifact safe, and for all to see.

About the Author

Rachael Smith is a UK-based comic creator whose books include *Quarantine Comix*, *Wired Up Wrong*, and *The Rabbit*. *Quarantine Comix* won Best Digital Comic at the 2021 Tripwire Awards, among other accolades. Rachael lives with her partner Rob, and cat Rufus.

Our heartfelt thanks to the Unbound backers listed below,
who have been with this book since the very beginning.

Thank you for your patience.

James Abraham

Dani Abram

Chris Addison

Glyn Allen

Gina Allnatt

Sally Amberton

Emily Armstrong

Kate Ashwin

Amy-Laura Austin

Robert Baldock

Jim Barker

Liv Bellamy-Brown

Richard Bennett

Jake Laverde

Lara Bettens

Alister Black

Ken Boswell

Steve Bowman

Norman Boyd

Paul Braidford

Dr Michael Brogan

Craig Brougham

Sophie Brown

Nick Bryan

Amy Caroline

Anthony Carrick

Jody Clarke

Jeremy Clarke

Scott Coello

Eliot Cole

Mike Collins

Timo Conrady

Nic Cook

Paul Cornell

Daniel Cox

Stephen Crabtree

Emma Craig-West

Daniel Crowley

Julia Croyden

Rob Cureton

Kev Davies

Hanako DeRitter

James Dickinson

Peter Duncan

Ian Edginton

Keith Falconer

Zhou Fang

Richard Francis

Martyn French

Sarah Gordon

Tali & Mog

Stuart Gould

Róisín Grasby

Paul Gregory

Peter Griffith

Claire Grinham

Paul Grummitt

Rebecca Harris

Lee Harris

Jonny Hart

Rebecca Haslam

Lorraine Hatchwell

Nicholas Hayes

Matt Hemsworth

Sasha-Jade Hornby

Hannah Howden

Ady Hunter

Lizzie Huxley-Jones

Judith Jackson

Andrew James

Sian Jefferson

Ollie Jones

deadmanjones

Rebecca Junell

Dan Katz

Lindsey Keegan

Wayne Kelly

Alan Kennedy

Dan Kieran

Stewart Killala

Jack Kirby-Lowe

Rose Kirk

Nicole Koschmeder

Ruth Krapp

Abe Kruger

Josie Kyriacou

Ralph Lachmann

Gary Lawson

Garth Leder

Andrew Leeke

Amy

Amelia Sheridan

Jennifer Liao